This book belongs to

_____

_____

_____

Asda's early readers are designed for you and your child to share; with exciting opportunities for your child to begin to read to you.

This old man is based on the well-known rhyme, which all children love. The rhyme is given on the left-hand page for the adult to read to the child. On the right-hand page, your child can join in by reading the text given in **bold.** Words from the rhyme are sometimes repeated, and new words are added to help your child to join in.

First read the book aloud. Then go through the rhyme again, this time encouraging your child to read the text on the right-hand page. The illustrations give picture cues to the words. Many young children will remember the words rather than be able to read them, but this is an important part of learning to read. Always praise as you go along – keep your reading sessions fun, and stop if your child loses interest.

Produced exclusively for
ASDA Stores Ltd
Great Wilson Street
Leeds LS11 5AD
by Ladybird Books Ltd
27 Wrights Lane London
W8 5TZ

This old man

by Karen Bryant-Mole
illustrated by John Blackman

ASDA

play and learn

This old man, he played one.
He played knick, knack
On his drum...

I like my drum.

With a knick, knack
Paddy whack
Give a dog a bone...

This old man came
Rolling home.

9

This old man, he played two.
He played knick, knack
On his shoe...

1

2

Are these my shoes?

11

This old man, he played three.
He played knick, knack
On his knee...

These are my knees.

This old man, he played four.
He played knick, knack
On the floor...

1

2

3

4

Look at me!

15

This old man, he played five.
He played knick, knack
Doing a dive...

I like to swim!

This old man, he played six.
He played knick, knack
With some sticks...

1
2
3
4
5
6

This dog likes sticks.

19

This old man, he played seven.
He played knick, knack
Up to heaven...

Up I go!

This old man, he played eight.
He played knick, knack
On his gate...

1
2
3
4
5
6
7
8

Here is my house.

23

This old man, he played nine.
He played knick, knack
On the line...

1
2
3
4
5
6
7
8
9

I have fun.

This old man, he played ten.
He played knick, knack
All over again.